To Mrs. Clarkin—
I hope you
always expect
a miracle!
Cyndi &
Marshall

Marshall
the miracle dog

A Picture Book Based on a True Story

Written by Cynthia Willenbrock
Illustrated by Lauren Heimbaugh

THE MARSHALL MOVEMENT™

Acknowledgements

My Parents—It is from you I am full of compassion and perseverance.

My Friends and Family—I believe in me because you do.

Humane Society of MO and Dr. Schwartz—For saving Marshall's life and countless others.

My Focus Group—For helping me dissect the manuscript and bring about powerful changes.

My Co-Workers at KellyMitchell—They all just GET me, and put up with me!

Debra Mostow Zakarin—My Manager/Agent—For being one of the most creative forces in the children's publishing industry and becoming the best cheerleader in my camp.

Charlotte and Mary Ellen, Special School District of St Louis County —For reinforcing the need to share Marshall's story.

Marie Harbers, Therapy Dog Trainer, PetSmart® and Spirit of St. Louis Chapter of Love on a Leash—For training Marshall as a Therapy Dog, allowing him to share his story EVERYWHERE!

Amy Chappuis—For writing a beautiful introduction capturing the essence of Marshall.

Lonnie Whitaker—fellow Author—For teaching me the "universe rewards movement."

Mike Bizelli—Photographer extraordinaire—For his courage and willingness to walk in the trenches and capture on film all the injustices.

Laurie Young—Art Director—For her creative spirit and inspiration.

Most of all for MARSHALL—He turned my life upside down the day he arrived and everything that was unimportant just fell away . . .

Library of Congress Control Number: 2012945239

ISBN 978-0-615-66625-9

10 9 8 7 6 5 4 3 2 1

Printed in the United States of America
First Edition

Designed by Laurie L. Young

A portion of the proceeds will go to Humane Society of Missouri.

Dedicated to the Defenseless . . . and those willing to defend.

—C.W.

"Marshall, Mooshy, Lulu! Come in!"

We charge for the back door. Mom is letting us know our long day of playing is over, and it's time for dinner. I have the best life today. But it hasn't always been this way. I remember clearly what it used to be like. . . .

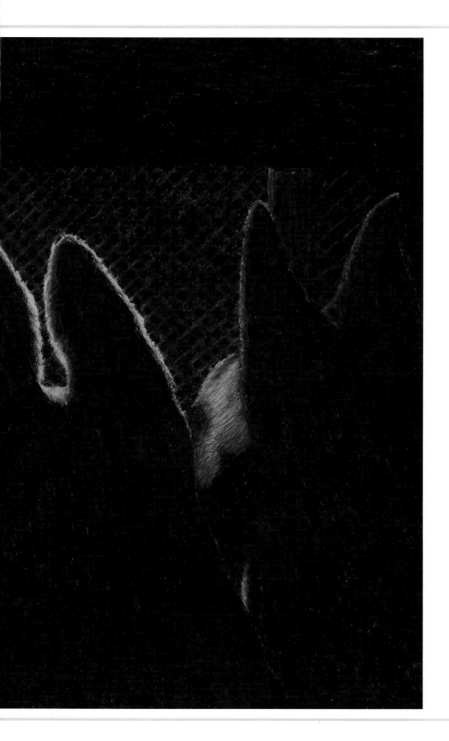

I awake that day with the same hungry belly I always wake up to. I think I must have had an awful nightmare about being bullied and attacked again by the other dogs. Then I look down into my empty dog bowl, see my reflection, and realize it was not just a bad dream.

There is a cut in the side of my face and bite marks all over my body. But worst of all, when I try to stand up I realize that this time, they have broken my leg.

This fighting is not new. Living with 60 other dogs in a small confined pen, we rarely get food. We are hungry all the time, sometimes eating dirt or hay just to fill our bellies.

We are living with an animal hoarder named Susan, who has more dogs than any person could ever take care of properly. When Susan's husband does come every so often with food, I try to stay out of the way of the meaner dogs in order to avoid fights. But yesterday, I needed to get a few kibbles to survive, and when I tried, the bullies attacked.

Now I am in so much pain I don't know what to do. What could I do? Nothing.

I just keep to myself in a corner in this dirty old pen and hope it does not happen again.

All alone, I start blaming myself. I wonder if the last attack is my fault. But I really didn't do anything bad! I just needed to eat. I waited for the others to make sure they were eating and tried to grab a few morsels of food. I didn't want much.

That was when I got attacked by the other poor, hungry dogs. They just wanted the same thing I did.

Now I am laying here in agony, wondering what will happen to me.

Days go by. . . . Another feeding comes. The pain in my face is awful. My broken and throbbing leg makes it almost impossible to get up for food or water. But I manage to crawl over to a bowl and get enough scraps to keep me going. I just don't know how much longer I can hang on.

I try to sleep the days away so I am not aware of my damaged body. I am trying so hard to keep my spirit alive. After I go back to sleep, I hear strange voices. Another dream? But then the barking and howling from the others wakes me up completely.

I realize something strange is going on.

These voices are not the voices I hear while being fed every once in a while by Susan's husband. No.

And there are so many voices at once! I've never heard so many different voices! What could be going on? As I lay in my corner of the filthy pen, I feel someone looking at me. I raise my face, but it takes me a long time to get the courage to actually look up.

I see a man with his mouth hanging open and his eyes wide like saucers. "Hey guys!" he yells. "Get in here fast! We gotta get this lil' guy to the hospital!"

But I have never been out of this pen. What are they going to do with me? Frightened, I begin to tremble. I curl up and try to hide my wounded face. Maybe they will forget about me and just go away.

Two big men carefully lift my fragile, abused body and lay me gently on a stretcher. They appear more frightened than I feel when they look down at my body. That alone scares me even more.

I try to jump down so I can run away, but realize it is useless. I don't have the strength with my broken front leg.

At that moment, I just give up. I allow them to take me away. I feel helpless. My spirit is crushed.

The men set me in the back of the Humane Society Rescue Squad van. I am being rescued! The others are being saved as well! We all are being removed from that filthy place where we went days without food and had very little water. We never had toys or beds or any love and attention from humans.

But where will we all go? What will they do to us now? And what will happen to me? Who would want a scrawny, dirty, ugly dog with fleas and all these bite marks and broken bones?

We pull up to the hospital, and they rush me in to the Operating Room. Once again I try to get up and run—and this time I almost make it. But they hold me down and start stroking my fur, telling me it is going to be all right.

I have never been petted before and, despite the pain, it feels good. I decide to let them do what needs to be done. That is when a team of doctors and nurses walk in to the Operating Room and gasp.

They begin by closely examining the gash in my face, all my bite marks, and my broken leg.

I hear one of the nurses ask, "Dr. Schwartz, do you think he'll make it?"

My ears perk up waiting for the answer.

The doctor replies, "Hard to say. This is the worst case I have ever seen. It would take a miracle."

Those are the last words I hear before they put me to sleep in order to perform surgery on my torn-up body.

I wake up in the recovery room feeling very groggy. I raise my head, and it takes me a moment to remember where I am. I scan the room and see a mirror. It's horrible! There is a scar across half of my face. I look so much like a monster I scare myself!

And then it gets worse. I look down and realize I no longer have one of my front legs.

I think, "How can this be?" and

"How will I run?" and

"How will I walk?" and

"How will the other dogs treat me?"

And then I think the worst thought ever: "How can I live like this?"

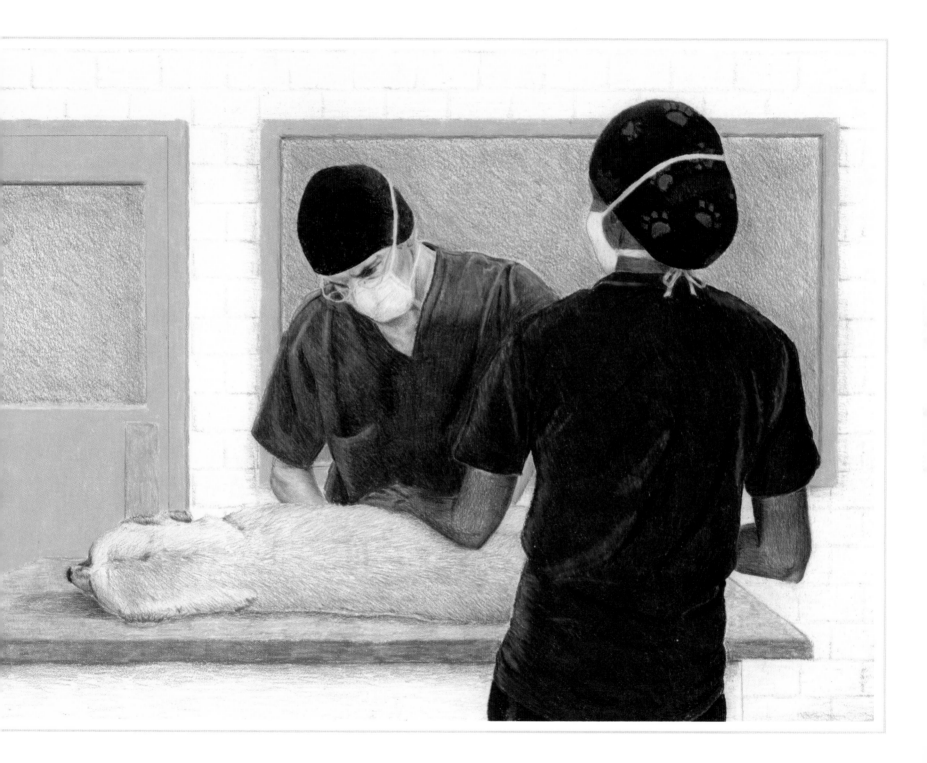

Dr. Schwartz walks in to the room asking, "How are you feeling, Marshall?"

I didn't know who he is talking to. Who is Marshall? I look around the room. I am the only dog here.

"I tell you what little guy: You are a dog with a very strong will to live. Everyone's calling you Marshall the Miracle Dog."

So they have given me a name. Marshall. It has a nice ring to it. I have never been given a name!

"You had quite a scare, but you're going to be just fine. Try to get some sleep. You're safe now."

And sleep I do. I feel like I sleep for a week.

When I finally do wake up, the nurses and doctors all want to teach me to walk again. They help lift me up, and I immediately topple over. This is terrible. I just know I will never walk again.

Jenny, my favorite nurse, must be reading my mind because she says, "Don't worry, Marshall. You'll be chasing after squirrels before you know it! We just need to do some therapy to get your strength and balance built up."

Jenny is right. Everyone at the Humane Society hospital rallies around me and takes me for short walks down the hallway several times a day.

A few weeks later, the doctor removes the stitches on my face.

Catching a glimpse in the mirror of myself, I think, "Not too bad, Doc. I still have my handsome doggy features and sweet puppy dog eyes." I feel much stronger in a very short time, and am soon able to go outside on real walks.

My nose goes crazy at first! The smell of trees, flowers, and grass is wonderful! Back in the pen, all we had was dirt, hay, and filth to sniff.

The love and attention everyone at the Humane Society showers on me makes me feel like a true celebrity. I can't even catch a good nap before someone else pops into my crate to give me love, treats, and lots of petting.

It slowly occurs to me that my belly hardly even has to grumble and food will just show up in my bowl! I never have to want for a meal around here. And my bed: It is so soft and cozy, and hard to leave after a long night's slumber.

A dog could get used to this!

After a few months, I overhear a couple of volunteers talking.

"Marshall has recovered just beautifully. I guess he'll be up for adoption soon."

My ears perk up. Adoption? Me?

I see the others around here leave with their tails wagging as their new owners take them to their Forever Homes. But they have all their legs and no scars. They look like normal dogs should.

Who would want me? I am damaged goods. Sure, many of the other dogs come from abused or neglected situations, but their scars are all inside. One look at me and you know something isn't right!

The talk of adoption goes on for weeks. I know the time is drawing nearer because I have regained enough strength, and my wounds have healed enough that I will no longer need daily medical care and therapy. And every day I become more and more anxious about leaving the Humane Society, the safest place I have ever known!

What if no one wants me? Or worse, what if they do but their home is as bad as where I came from? That's just too terrible to think about.

And then the day comes. They come to tell me I am ready to be adopted into a loving Forever Home.

I am not ready for this. I start to shake and lower my head, feeling almost as frightened as the day of my rescue—all those thoughts about the unknown!

I overhear them talking about how my new mom saw a video the Humane Society made about me and my story. They say my new mom had tears in her eyes while watching the video and she said she just fell in love with me. Well, we will see about that.

I am so afraid she will not want me after she meets me and sees the true extent of my former abuse and neglect.

Jenny, the nurse, comes to put on my collar and leash. "Well Marshall, you've been a true gift and inspiration to us all around here. We all learned a lot about how to hold on and how to get back on your feet even when you've seen the darkest days." I see tears falling from her eyes when she finishes saying, "I will miss you, my little Miracle Dog. But you have a Forever Home to go to where you will be loved and cared for."

The time has arrived. I let Jenny walk me out. My legs are shaking. My entire body is trembling. I am scared.

My new mom is in the lobby waiting for me. It is a long three-legged walk—or should I say hop—down the hallway to get to her. There are lines of workers and volunteers all wanting to wish me well and give me one last pat on the head. Some even rub on my nub where my fourth leg used to be.

When I finally reach her, my head hangs low to hide the scar. My new mom sits down on the floor and lifts my face. She kisses me right on the nose! It's like she can't even see my scars.

Then she sits me on her lap and smells me and strokes my fur. She rubs where my front leg used to be.

And just like that, I know she loves me just the way I am.

And I know I love her. Just the way she is.

In the parking lot of the Humane Society, Mom picks me up (boy she is strong!) and carefully places me in the back seat as we embark on the journey to my new Forever Home.

On the drive she keeps talking about Mooshy: How excited Mooshy is to meet me. And how much fun Mooshy and I will have playing together. And how Mooshy can teach me the tricks he's learned.

It finally dawns on me that Mooshy is a dog— and he lives at my new home, too!

Instantly, the fear sets in. Once again the racing thoughts start: "What if he laughs at me?" and

"What if he ignores me?" and

"What if he bullies me or attacks me like some of the other dogs?"

I don't think this is such a good idea after all.

Mom pulls in to the driveway. She comes around and gently lifts me out of the back seat, careful to not let me jump and risk hurting my one good front leg.

Walking me to the back yard, she takes off my leash and allows me to sniff around and get used to my new surroundings. There are toys and balls everywhere.

Then I hear the bark from inside. Mooshy! Uh oh, this may not go so well. . . .

Mom opens the door to let Mooshy out. He barrels down the steps toward me. I cower, and he skids to a stop right in front of me. I wince, not sure what will happen next.

He begins to sniff me. I let him, careful not to move. I am petrified. Mooshy must have sensed this because he walks away, grabs a ball, and drops it at my paw. Then he runs away so I will chase him.

I have grown up with many dogs, so being around dogs is nothing new. But this playful spirit called Mooshy is definitely different! Where I come from in the pen, we were all so hungry and neglected that there was no energy left over for playing.

A new feeling of freedom washes over me. There's no pen here! I begin to chase Mooshy. Mom sits there watching and crying and tossing the ball while Mooshy and I play together. I didn't know there was this much joy in the world.

I love my new home.

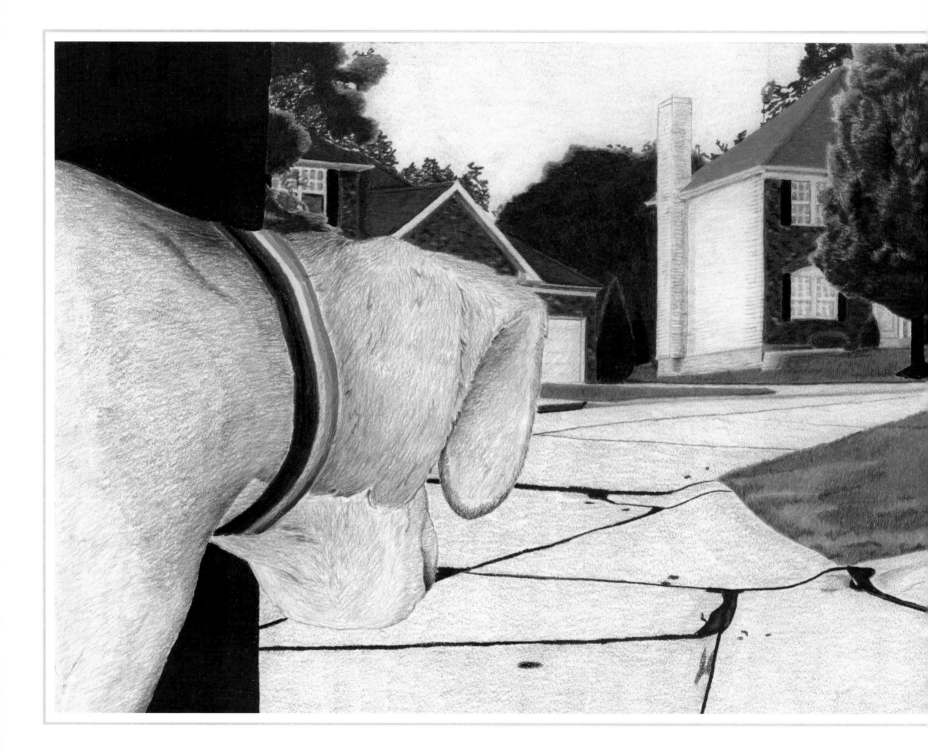

Mooshy teaches me so much over the next few days. I have never been in a house before with carpet and furniture . . . and shoes! Lots and lots of shoes. Mooshy shows me what toys are mine to chew on, and what belongs to Mom and is not for chewing.

He shows me how to let Mom know I have to go potty.

When it is feeding time, Mooshy teaches me what is his and what is mine, that there is enough, and that we don't need to fret or fight at mealtimes.

But there are certain things Mooshy cannot teach me. Such as, how to walk on tile floors without sliding or how to climb up or down steps with only three legs.

Mooshy also cannot prepare me for what dogs in the outside world will think about me with my limitations.

I am so afraid to find out.

Our home is in a large neighborhood full of other dogs and children. Mom starts taking me for walks right away. She says she wants to "socialize" me. It feels more like she wants to "torture" me.

What if the kids all point and laugh? What if the other dogs look down their snouts at me? I can just hear the children now.

"What happened to his other leg?"

"Why does his face have a huge scar on it?"

"What's wrong with that dog?"

Why can't I just stay in the yard where I am safe from teasing? Why do I have to "socialize" anyway?

One day on our afternoon walk, I recognize the dog being walked toward us. I stiffen my legs. I would recognize his smell anywhere. That dog is one of the bullies from the pen! What are the chances of his being adopted and ending up living on my street? Oh no! What is going to happen now?

I hide behind Mom as his new mom walks him closer. Before I know it the bully is next to me, obviously recognizing me as well.

I shudder, waiting for an attack. To my amazement, he licks me right on the cheek where he had left a scar from our days in the pen.

I can see the look of sorry in his eyes.

I know right away that he is no longer a bully. It occurs to me that anyone can change once their needs are met and they are shown love.

Mom insists on the forced walks every day. All I really want to do is please her, so I go, always waiting for the teasing, but it never comes.

Sure, there are children who ask tough questions about me, and there are curious looks from grownups. But cruel remarks? Not a one.

It is just the opposite. Humans seem to love me because of my scars, as if they know I'm needier than most dogs. So they just pet me up more and more.

And the other dogs are the most surprising of all: It's as if they don't notice a massive scar on my cheek. It's as if they are all thinking, "Three legs? Oh, I didn't even notice. Let's go play."

Then one day, I meet her. I meet Lulu.

Mom's friend, Gertrude, has brought over Lulu for a playdate. Lulu is beautiful, with long, flowing black hair and a bright pink collar. At first glance my heart swells with love.

I think for sure that she and Mooshy will hit it off—after all, he is so handsome with his shiny coat, not a hair out of place.

But strangely, all her attention is on me. It is me she wants to play with. It is my neck she nips at. It is me she canoodles with in the sunshine! It is me she loves. ME! Three-legged me!

It is true that I had a rough start to my life back in the pen. Each day passed so slowly. My rumbling belly ached for food and my constant prayer was that there would not be another attack.

It is true that I never received any attention, or exercise, or had any fun.

And even though there were 60 dogs in the pen, I had no friends. Everyone was just fending for himself or herself, trying to make it through yet another day. It was a joyless existence.

But the day the Humane Society rescued me they gave me a new life—and even a real name. From that day forward, the doctors fixed my injuries and I began to heal. I never miss a meal. I have more toys and chew bones than I can count. I have a soft bed. I have a beautiful home with a mom and a brother. I even have a best friend.

Most importantly, I have unconditional love and acceptance—exactly as I am.

Doctor Schwartz was right. To come from brokenness to the life I have today is nothing short of a miracle.

HAPPY FOREVER HOMES

Rescue dogs adopted from the HSMO in 2011-2012: (left to right) *Sunshine,* 4 year old, adopted 2/20/2012. *Tinsel,* 1 year old, adopted 2/27/2012. *Walter,* 5 year old, adopted 1/4/2012. *Nico,* 1 year old, adopted 2/4/2012. *Maggie,* 6 year old, adopted 2/28/2012. *Dave,* 5 year old, adopted 5/7/2011. *Cartmen,* 8 year old, adopted 1/21/2012. *Keisha,* 4 year old, adopted 10/15/2011. *Neyo,* 3 year old, adopted 2/15/2012. *Gladys,* 8 year old, adopted 10/23/2011. *Oswald,* 4 year old, adopted 2/25/2012. *Cal,* 7 year old, adopted 1/23/2012. *Aries,* 3 year old, adopted 10/13/2011. *Llewellyn,* 4 year old, adopted 9/18/2011. *Crystal,* 3 year old, adopted 8/22/2011. *Bingo,* 2 year old, adopted 4/15/2011. *Molly,* 3 year old, adopted 11/16/2011. *Missy,* 11 month old, adopted 7/8/2011. *Bernice,* 7 year old, adopted 7/22/2011. *CC,* 1 year old, adopted 3/12/2011. *Ramona,* 2 year old, adopted 2/2/2012. *Alsavador,* 7 year old, adopted 10/01/2011. *Pepper,* 8 year old, adopted 6/11/2011. *Cotton,* 6 year old, adopted 8/29/2011. *Mason,* 8 year old, adopted 8/10/2011. *Nay Nay,* 2 year old, adopted 1/20/2012. *Bernie,* 3 year old, adopted 2/24/2011. *Magdalen,* 5 year old, adopted 8/27/2011. *Nancy,* 2 year old, adopted 2/15/2012. *John,* 2 year old, adopted 8/17/2011.

Afterword

I was not prepared for what I saw the day Marshall and I met.

Marshall was among the first to be carried from the van, a distinction reserved for the most critically injured. As we lifted him ever so gingerly to the exam table I stared in disbelief at the gaping wounds on his face, and exposed muscles and bones stared back at me. How could any human being have ignored the sight of his condition, or the twisted front leg that dangled lifelessly from his side? And how could anyone have neglected his sad brown eyes' plea for help? Marshall was finally where he belonged, but I still worried that even the most well-intentioned veterinary team was unlikely to save him now. And yet we owed it to Marshall and to ourselves to do everything in our power to give him a chance.

Marshall was dehydrated and dangerously thin. He had infection in the shattered bones of his foreleg and throughout his bloodstream. We treated him intensively with fluids, with antibiotics and with medicine for his pain. He had multiple surgeries. His heart stopped on the operating table on more than one occasion. It became clear throughout his phenomenal recovery that Marshall had not read the same books as his doctors and nurses. He did not give up his fight, and we were proud to be in his corner throughout. He survived the unsurvivable. And as we saw Marshall slowly regain his strength, we felt him lift the spirits of all who worked so hard to save him.

Steven Schwartz, VMD
Director of Veterinary Services
Humane Society of Missouri

Humane Society of Missouri Mission Statement

Established in 1870, the Humane Society of Missouri (HSMO) is one of the oldest and largest animal welfare organizations in the United States. Dedicated to second chances, HSMO provides a safe and caring haven to abused, neglected and abandoned animals. Its mission is to end the cycle of abuse and pet overpopulation through its Animal Cruelty Task Force, spay/neuter programs and humane education program. HSMO is committed to creating lasting relationships between people and animals through their adoption programs and nationally accredited veterinary medical clinics. www.hsmo.org